Goldilocks
and the three
Bears

Retold by Ian Robinson

Illustrated by Gerry Embleton

award publications limited

Printed in Belgium

ISBN 0 86163 007 6
© Award Publications Ltd. 1980
Spring House, Spring Place,
London NW5. England

Once upon a time there was a little girl called Goldilocks. She lived with her parents in a house on the very edge of a great forest. She was called Goldilocks because every time the sun shone her beautiful hair gleamed like gold. But, although she looked as good as gold, Goldilocks was really a very naughty little girl who was always up to some sort of mischief.

Her parents were very kind to her and gave her everything she ever wanted, but Goldilocks was never satisfied for long. She soon grew tired of playing with her new toys and would leave them lying all over the floor until they got broken. When she was bored Goldilocks would just sit in her room and sulk.

"How nice they look," she thought to herself, "I wonder if they are ripe enough to eat?" The next moment she climbed over the fence and picked one, it was delicious, so good that Goldilocks reached out and took another to eat on her way.

At the end of the orchard, Goldilocks came to the forest where her mother had warned her not to go. The trees grew taller than houses and only a narrow winding path led forward into the gloom.

"I'm not afraid," said Goldilocks. "It all looks perfectly safe to me." And she set off through the trees, deep into the middle of the forest.

When Goldilocks had been walking through the forest for some time and her eyes were used to the dark, she saw the most peculiar little house set into the twisted roots of an old oak tree. She went closer and pressed her nose to the window, "I wonder what it's like inside?" she said. As there seemed to be no-one in sight, she opened a window and climbed inside for a better look.

Inside the house everything was clean and tidy, with low, sloping ceilings and a log fire which kept it nice and warm. Goldilocks decided to sit in a chair and rest for a few minutes before going home. First she sat in a great big chair which stood all alone in the corner. "Oh that's much too hard," she said. Next she sat in a smaller chair with a lovely big cushion but she found this one too soft.

Finally Goldilocks sat in the smallest chair of all, but it was too small and broke as soon as she sat down.

"No matter," said Goldilocks, "I'll just see what's in this room through this little door."

So Goldilocks went through the door and found herself in a tiny kitchen where three bowls of porridge were set to cool on the table. The sight of the porridge made Goldilocks very hungry and she wondered how it tasted.

"I'll just try a little to see if it is cool enough," she said. First, she tried the largest bowl, but it had too much salt. Next, she tried the middle-sized bowl, but it was far too sweet. Then Goldilocks tried the smallest bowl of all, "that's just right," she said, and finished it off.

Goldilocks thought that she would like to see upstairs so she slowly climbed the staircase.

There she found three beds, one big, one medium-sized and one small one. "I wonder if these are very comfortable!" Goldilocks thought, and she lay down on each bed in turn to find out.

The first bed was too hard for Goldilocks. "Oh no," she said, "I couldn't sleep on this bed." Then she tried the next bed which was covered in pretty patterns. Although the bed looked very nice, Goldilocks found it just too soft. "Oh dear," she sighed, "I couldn't sleep there either."

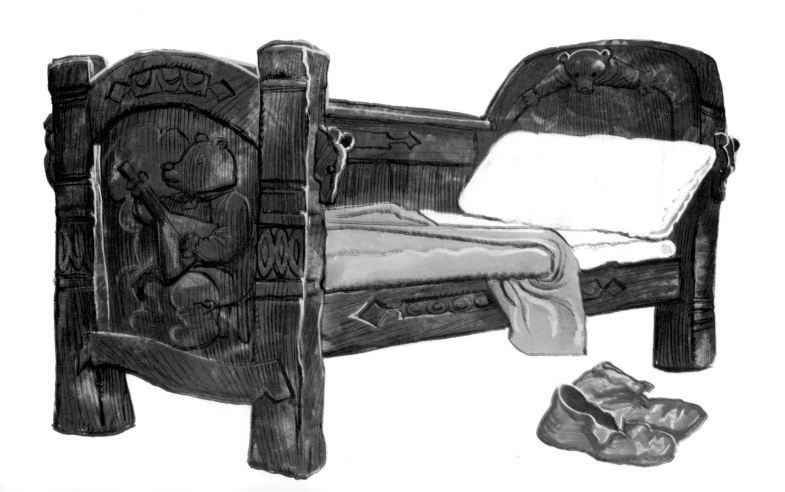

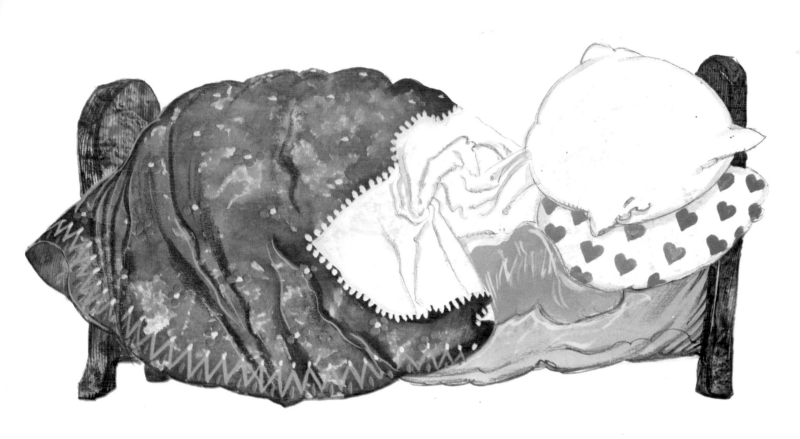

That left the smallest bed and as soon as
she lay down on it Goldilocks knew that it was just
right for her. In fact, she soon fell fast asleep.

At that moment, the three bears who lived in the little house were coming home from collecting firewood in the forest.

"I do hope my porridge is ready now," said baby bear to his mother as their house came into view.

At this Goldilocks woke up and was surprised to see the three bears gathered round Baby Bear's bed. She was so frightened that she jumped out of bed at once and ran down the stairs and out of the house as fast as her legs would carry her. She didn't stop running until she was back through the forest and safely home.

"How extraordinary!" exclaimed Father Bear, "I expect the little girl got lost in the forest and came across our house by accident."

"She must have been very clumsy," said Baby Bear, looking at all the mess Goldilocks had made.

"I think that she lost her glasses in the forest and kept on bumping into things," said his mother. "Why, she didn't seem to notice us at all!"

Meanwhile Goldilocks had learned her lesson. "I'll never be so careless again," she sobbed and set about tidying up her room before her mother came home from the village. Do you know, that from that day onwards she was never bored or restless again and her room was almost as neat and tidy as the three bears' little house.